A New Life

Vocabulary Words

unclean **un**able **un**clear cabin journey statue

[1] Nikko was tired of being on a ship. At first, it had been fun. Now it was crowded, smelly, and unclean. The air was fresh on deck, but all he could see were miles and miles of water.

[2] "Life will be better in America," he thought. "Papa is waiting for us there. I cannot wait to see him."

[3] Nikko turned to Mama. "When will we get to America?" he asked.

[4] "Soon," said Mama. "See the birds flying in the sky? That means we are close to land."

[5] "Good," said Nikko. "This has been a long journey. We have been at sea for almost two weeks. Do you think we will ever go back to Greece?"

[6] "I don't think we will. We will start a new life in America," said Mama. "Now let's go below to the cabin. We need to get some sleep. We will have much to do when we get there."

[7] Nikko rolled up his coat to make a pillow. At first, he was unable to sleep. It was warm in the cabin. He was afraid and excited at the same time. Would he like America? Would it be strange?

[8] Nikko closed his eyes. He thought about his old home. He tried to picture his new home. It was unclear what America would be like. He wondered if it would be like Greece. Would he feel like a visitor, or would it feel like home?

[9] Nikko woke to the sound of the ship's horn. "Mama," shouted Nikko. "We are here! We are in America! Let's go up on deck."

GO ON

A New Life (continued)

[10] "Look at the Statue of Liberty!" shouted Nikko. "It is the biggest statue that I have ever seen."

[11] "It is beautiful," said Mama happily. "I cannot wait to start our new life here."

[12] Nikko and his mother were in America. They would stop at Ellis Island before starting their new life. They had come to a land with new hopes and dreams.

from "A New Life"

Nikko rolled up his coat to make a pillow. At first, he was unable to sleep. It was warm in the cabin. He was afraid and excited at the same time. Would he like America? Would it be strange?

Nikko closed his eyes. He thought about his old home. He tried to picture his new home. It was unclear what America would be like. He wondered if it would be like Greece. Would he feel like a visitor, or would it feel like home?

Travel to America

Long ago, people came to America on ships. At first, the ships had sails. The trip across the ocean would take about three months. Later, the sailing ships were replaced with ships powered by steam. The steam was made by burning coal. Steamships took about two weeks to cross the ocean. Today, people still come to America on ships. However, many more people travel on airplanes. The trip takes only hours.

Ellis Island

Vocabulary Words

unhappy **re**turn **re**tell immigrants museum tour

[1] People who move from one country to make their home in another country are called immigrants. Immigrants hope for a better life in the new country. Often, they move because they are unhappy in their own country.

[2] In the 1800s, people came to America to start new lives. They came on ships. They came in great numbers. These people were immigrants.

[3] When the people saw the Statue of Liberty, they knew they had arrived. Then they would board small boats. The boats took the people to Ellis Island.

[4] On Ellis Island, the immigrants would have to wait in long lines. Their names were written down. Doctors made sure they were not sick. The men had to show they could get a job. Women and children had to show that they had someone waiting for them.

[5] Why did these people make the long trip to the United States? They wanted to be free. They wanted good jobs. They wanted the chance to make a good life. They did not want to return to their old country.

[6] Today, Ellis Island is a museum. Visitors can take a tour. The tour includes a room where immigrants slept. Objects are on display. The objects include bags, clothing, tickets, and many other things left behind by the immigrants.

[7] Visitors can listen to music from the time. A play, a film, and other shows retell the stories of the immigrants. Photos and posters are used to show what life was like. All the names of immigrants who came to Ellis Island are written on a wall in the museum.

GO ON

Ellis Island (continued)

[8] The Ellis Island Museum is an interesting place to visit. It gives everyone a chance to find out what it was like to be an immigrant on Ellis Island.

from "Ellis Island"

Today, Ellis Island is a museum. Visitors can take a tour. The tour includes a room where immigrants slept. Objects are on display. The objects include bags, clothing, tickets, and many other things left behind by the immigrants.

Visitors can listen to music from the time. A play, a film, and other shows retell the stories of the immigrants. Photos and posters are used to show what life was like. All the names of immigrants who came to Ellis Island are written on a wall in the museum.

Annie Moore

Annie Moore stepped off her ship. She heard bells and whistles. The place was covered in red, white, and blue decorations. What was happening? An official came up to Annie. He told her that she was the very first immigrant to stop at Ellis Island.

Annie arrived with her two brothers. She was only 15 years old. Today, a statue of Annie is at Ellis Island in memory of her.

The Statue of Liberty

Vocabulary Words

renew **a**top **a**shore friendship harbor symbol

[1] The Statue of Liberty stands tall and bright in New York Harbor. Her yellow torch welcomes people to America. Travelers on big ships entering the harbor are happy to see her.

[2] The Statue of Liberty was a gift from France. France gave America the statue as a sign of friendship. The statue was built in Paris. Workers took it apart. They sent the pieces to America on a ship. The statue was in 350 pieces. The pieces were taken ashore on Liberty Island in New York Harbor. Workers put the Statue of Liberty together again.

[3] The Statue of Liberty stands near to Ellis Island. Long ago, Ellis Island was the first place some immigrants stopped before they entered our country. The statue was the first thing they saw as their ship arrived in New York.

[4] The Statue of Liberty is one of our country's best-known statues. The huge statue is over 300 feet tall. Copper sheets cover her body. She looks as if she is wearing flowing robes. The seven spikes atop her head stand for the seven seas and landmasses. Her right hand holds a flame that stands for freedom.

[5] People traveled a long way to see the Statue of Liberty. Visitors would climb 350 steps to reach the top. There are windows in her crown. People standing there could see for miles. They could see New York City and the harbor.

[6] The Statue of Liberty is over 100 years old. For her 100th birthday, workers cleaned the statue. They fixed her body and flame. Workers used many tools. They worked long and hard to renew her.

GO ON

The Statue of Liberty (continued)

[7] The Statue of Liberty is pictured on stamps. The statue is also pictured on coins and bills. Children learn about her at school. Americans are very proud of the Statue of Liberty. She is the symbol of freedom.

from "The Statue of Liberty"

The Statue of Liberty was a gift from France. France gave America the statue as a sign of friendship. The statue was built in Paris. Workers took it apart. They sent the pieces to America on a ship. The statue was in 350 pieces. The pieces were taken ashore on Liberty Island in New York Harbor. Workers put the Statue of Liberty together again.

A New Home

The small boy held his sister's hand tightly. They were very happy. They were a little bit scared, too. They stood on the big ship's deck. They could see a great statue of a lady. She was standing on an island. She was smiling. She wore a crown. She held a bright light. She seemed to be saying, "Welcome to America!"

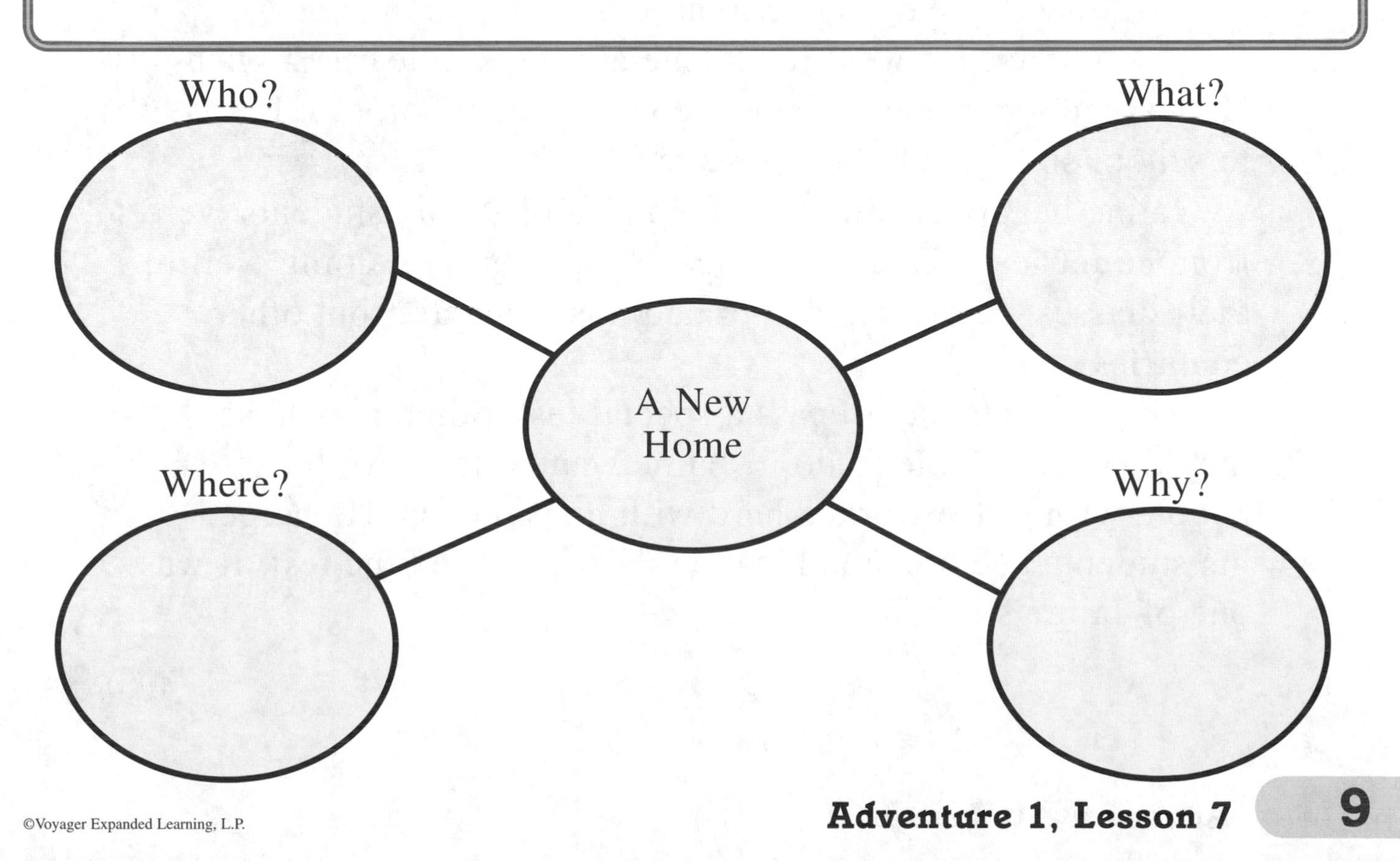

An American Dream

Vocabulary Words

aboard speak**er** learn**er** challenge college reason

[1] Many people move to the United States. They come from other countries. Most people have a good reason for moving. Some people want to get away from unkind leaders in their country. Some people come to look for work. Some want a better life. Jaime Escalante came to this country to follow his dreams.

[2] Jaime lived in South America. He was a teacher in a small village. But he was not happy. He wanted to live and teach in the United States. He wanted to meet new people. He wanted to see new places and try new things. He and his family went aboard a ship and traveled to California.

[3] Jaime faced a huge challenge in his new home. He could not work as a teacher because he could not speak English. However, he had to make a living to support his family. He worked during the days. He took jobs as a cook and as a factory worker. He went to college at nights to learn English. He learned more about his new country at school, too. He went to school so he could become a teacher here.

[4] Jaime began teaching at a high school. Many students were from countries in South America. Some were not doing well in their classes. Jaime decided to help his students from other countries.

[5] The students had to pass a special test. Some people said they'd never be able to do it. Jaime wanted to prove those people wrong. He worked hard with his students. He helped his students become good learners. They passed the test. It was one of Jaime's brightest days!

An American Dream (continued)

[6] Some people made a movie to tell Jaime's story. The movie shows what a good teacher can do.

[7] Jaime Escalante became a speaker, too. He talked about his teaching ideas. He received many awards. They were given to him for his good work.

from "An American Dream"

Many people move to the United States. They come from other countries. They move here for many different reasons. Some people want to get away from unkind leaders in their country. Some people come to look for work. Some want a better life. Jaime Escalante came to this country to follow his dreams.

Alexander Graham Bell

Alexander Graham Bell was born in Scotland. He moved to America when he was a young man.

Bell liked to make new things. He invented the first phone. He used everyday things in his inventions.

Bell was a teacher, too. He taught children who could not hear. Bell made a difference in his new country.

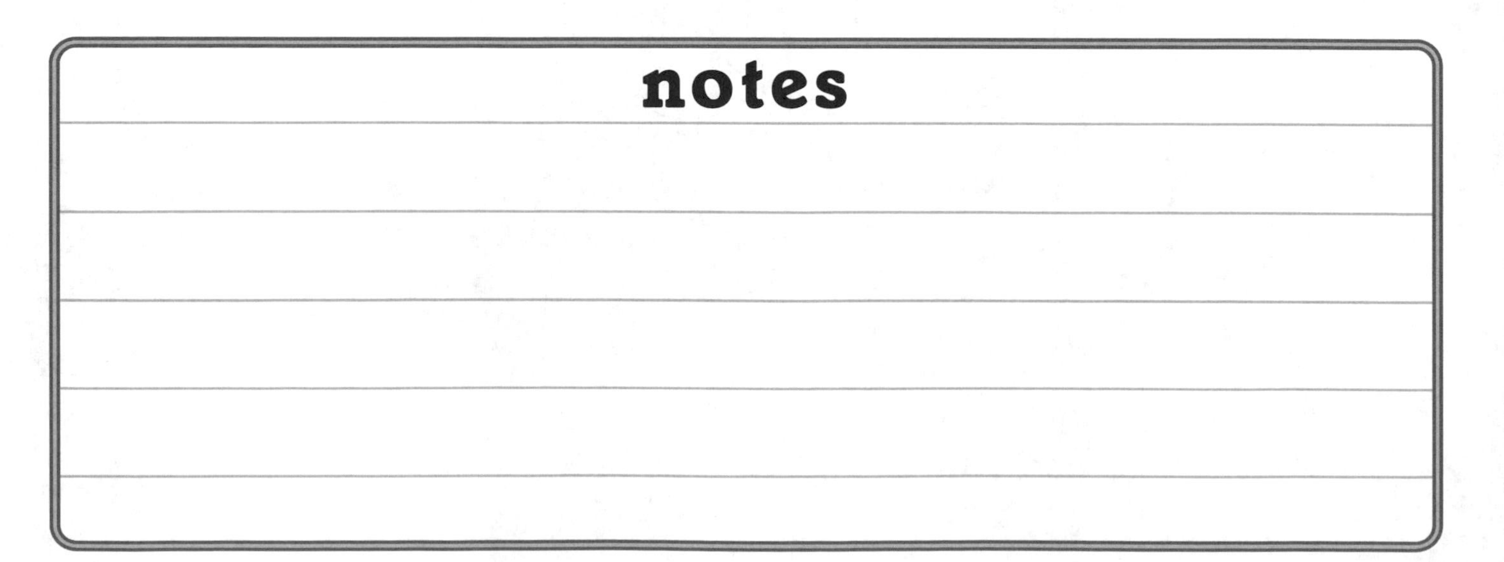

America's Pioneers

Vocabulary Words

farm**er** brave**ly** glad**ly** curious inventors scarce

[1] Pioneers are people who are the first to do things. The first person in space was called a pioneer. Inventors are pioneers, too. For Americans, though, the word brings to mind a special meaning. Pioneers were the people who settled the country. Most pioneers lived in the 1800s. They traveled west. They left safe homes. They looked for new lands. Some pioneers traveled across the whole country. They faced unknown things bravely. When they liked a place, they settled there. Each settler built a home. Settlers built new towns. They made new lives.

[2] Pioneers crossed the frontier. But the frontier kept moving. To the first pioneers, Ohio was "out west." By 1800, settlers had reached the Mississippi River. What would they do next? They kept right on going. They went to the Pacific Ocean. They settled the West.

[3] Most pioneers were farmers. They could live off the land. They were strong. They liked the outdoors. They could live without neighbors. They could grow their own food. A farmer made a good pioneer.

[4] All pioneers were not farmers, though. New towns grew. They needed all kinds of people. Every town wanted a doctor. Towns needed storekeepers, too. Just about everyone had a horse. That meant that every town needed a blacksmith. All kinds of people were pioneers.

GO ON

America's Pioneers (continued)

[5] Why did people want to become pioneers? Some moved because they wanted to see new things. For some, moving from place to place was in their blood. Others were running away. Moving to a new place meant a new start. Some left their old homes because jobs were scarce or their crops failed. They hoped for better luck in a new place. These people gladly left their old homes. Many pioneers were just plain curious. They could read about the West, but that wasn't enough. They could hear stories from a traveler, but that wasn't enough, either. Pioneers had to see the new land for themselves.

from "America's Pioneers"

Why did people want to become pioneers? Some moved because they wanted to see new things. For some, moving from place to place was in their blood. Others were running away. Moving to a new place meant a new start. Some left their old homes because jobs were scarce or their crops failed. They hoped for better luck in a new place. These people gladly left their old homes. Many pioneers were just plain curious. They could read about the West, but that wasn't enough. They could hear stories from a traveler, but that wasn't enough, either. Pioneers had to see the new land for themselves.

Laura Ingalls Wilder

Laura Ingalls Wilder was a true pioneer. She was born in 1867. Early in her life, Laura's family began traveling. Pa liked to move on, and so did Laura. As a child, she lived in many places. She lived on lonely farms far from other people. She lived in new towns. In 1879, the family stopped for good. They settled in the Dakota Territory. There Laura married. She and her husband moved a few more times. Then they built a home in Missouri. After that, Laura stayed in one place. She lived there for the rest of her life. She wrote the *Little House* books there. Laura died in 1957.

Wagon Train

Vocabulary Words

bright**ly** hard**est** hott**est** chores fetch stumbled

[1] Jeb heard animals outside. He smiled in his sleep. It must be his pony Bessie. Then Jeb remembered that Bessie was gone. Lots of his favorite things were gone. They had been sold. Papa needed money to buy a wagon. And the wagon didn't hold much. The family only could keep things they really needed. Jeb's family was about to become a pioneer family. Today they were heading west to find a new life.

[2] Jeb stumbled to the door. The sun was rising. Jeb saw friends outside. His grandparents were there, too. Jeb threw on his clothes and ran outside. He hugged Grandma tightly. Saying good-bye was the hardest thing he had ever done. He realized he might be seeing these people for the last time. Jeb climbed into the back of the wagon, and the family was off.

[3] Jeb didn't stay in the wagon long. The ride was bumpy and uncomfortable. Soon he was walking. Jeb was used to hard work. He'd always done his share of farm chores. But walking on the rutted road was hard. The sun shone brightly. It was the hottest day Jeb could remember. He was glad when lunchtime came.

[4] After lunch, the family rested. Then they moved on again. Their plan was to meet up with other families who were also traveling west. Soon a whole group of wagons was traveling together. Everyone stopped in late afternoon. They had traveled twelve miles.

[5] Jeb and his sister went to fetch water and gather firewood. Mama started dinner while Papa cared for the animals. After dinner, Jeb made some new friends.

Wagon Train (continued)

[6] Night fell. The grown-ups sang beside the campfire. In the middle of a song, Jeb's eyes closed. He was tired but happy. This trip might be fun. For a long time to come, all the days would be just like this one. When would the trip end? And where? Jeb didn't know, but he did know one thing. He couldn't wait to see what would happen.

from "Wagon Train"

After lunch, the family rested. Then they moved on again. Their plan was to meet up with other families who were also traveling west. Soon a whole group of wagons was traveling together. Everyone stopped in late afternoon. They had traveled twelve miles.

from "America's Pioneers"

Pioneers crossed the frontier. But the frontier kept moving. To the first pioneers, Ohio was "out west." By 1800, settlers had reached the Mississippi River. What would they do next? They kept right on going. They went to the ocean. They settled the West.

Finish the paragraph that tells what this passage is about.

Pioneers traveled across the frontier. ________________________

____

____

____

____

____

Pioneers kept on going until they had settled the whole country.

Pioneer Children's Games

Pioneer children were not so different from you and your friends. In pioneer times, some girls liked playing with dolls. They made their own dolls from cornhusks or old clothes. Pioneer boys often made their toys, too. Many boys carved toys out of wood. Pioneer children played some of the same games that you play today. They flew kites. Just like today, pioneer girls and boys played hide-and-seek. They also played checkers.

Write in order the important ideas from the passage.

Home at Last

Vocabulary Words

prettiest	purchased	outside	expand	glimpse	notches

[1] The wagon rolled to a stop. Sallie got her first glimpse of the land Pa had purchased. Sallie had been traveling for months. She was ready to settle down.

[2] Sallie couldn't wait to live in a house again. She would have to wait, though. Before Pa could start a house, he had to plant crops. All day, Pa chopped trees to clear a field. Ma and Sallie worked right beside him. It was the hardest work Sallie had ever done. At night, they slept in the wagon. Only one thing was different. Now the wagon was not moving. Every night, Sallie asked, "When will we have a house?"

[3] The long days passed. Pa chopped trees and hauled logs to the stream. Ma plowed, and Sallie cleared away rocks. At night, the family was almost too tired to talk. But Sallie always had enough energy for one question. "Will we begin the new house tomorrow, Pa?" Pa's answer was always no.

[4] Then one day, the field was cleared. Pa traveled to town and returned with seeds. All day, the family planted. That night, Sallie spoke up again. "What about the house, Pa?" she asked. Pa just winked.

[5] The next day, three of Sallie's new neighbors showed up early. The men started to work. They chopped notches in logs and stacked them on top of one another. Pa and the men worked quickly. By late afternoon, the house was finished. Pa hung the door, and Sallie hurried inside. The floor was made of dirt. A real wooden floor would come later. Later, the house would expand. Sallie and Ma would make rugs and curtains.

Home at Last (continued)

[6] To Sallie, the house was the prettiest one she had ever seen. She trotted back outside and ran to the field. There she gathered wildflowers. She carried them inside and placed them in a pitcher of water. “Beautiful flowers,” she exclaimed, “for our beautiful new home!”

Pioneer Quilts

New things were scarce on the frontier. Pioneers used things over and over. When the family's clothing wore out, the women and girls mended it. If a piece of clothing was too worn to mend, they cut it up. They used some parts for rags, but they saved the nicest pieces. When they had enough pieces, they sewed them together to make a warm, beautiful quilt. One morning, Sallie put on her favorite dress. It was too tight and too short. Her arms stuck out of the sleeves. Ma looked hard at the pretty material. She would make Sallie a new dress. She knew just what she would do with the old one.

from "Home at Last"

[1] The long days passed. Pa chopped trees and hauled logs to the stream. Ma plowed, and Sallie cleared away rocks. At night, the family was almost too tired to talk. But Sallie always had enough energy for one question. "Will we begin the new house tomorrow, Pa?" Pa's answer was always no.

[2] Then one day, the field was cleared. Pa traveled to town and returned with seeds. All day, the family planted. That night, Sallie spoke up again. "What about the house, Pa?" she asked. Pa just winked.

[3] The next day, three of Sallie's new neighbors showed up early. The men started to work. They chopped notches in logs and stacked them on top of one another. Pa and the men worked quickly. By late afternoon, the house was finished. Pa hung the door, and Sallie hurried inside. The floor was made of dirt. A real wooden floor would come later. Later, the house would expand. Sallie and Ma would make rugs and curtains.

Pioneer Schools

Vocabulary Words

winter summer grammar generation memorizing signal

[1] Pioneer children thought they were lucky to go to school. Many pioneers did not have a school. The ones who did often had to walk a great distance to and from school. Some children rode ponies. School didn't last all year. School was only open in summer and winter. It was only open then if the town had a teacher. In spring and fall, children had to stay home. Their families needed them. The children had to help work the farm.

[2] When pioneer children did have a school, it was a one-room schoolhouse. It was hot in summer and cold in winter. All the heat came from a small wood-burning stove. One teacher taught children of all ages. The teacher sometimes had help, though. The oldest students often helped the younger ones with their schoolwork.

[3] School supplies were hard to come by. Children wrote on slates. They could erase the slates. Then they could use them again. Books were scarce, too. Children brought books they had at home. They did not have many. Families were proud to own books. They were used over and over again by the children in the family. Sometimes they were handed down to the next generation.

[4] Children in pioneer schools learned only a few subjects. Reading, writing, and math were most important. Students also learned history. Much of the school day was spent memorizing. Students learned math facts and poems by heart. They learned dates and grammar rules by heart, too.

Pioneer Schools (continued)

[5] Like today, most children enjoyed lunchtime. Most lived too far from school to go home. They brought their lunch in pails. Lunchtime was the time to relax. The children ate and played games together. When lunchtime was over, the teacher rang a bell. That was the signal to stop playing and start working again.

Moving On

Dear Grandma,

When you get this letter, we will have moved on. We're heading west again. Ma says Pa won't be happy until he sees the Pacific Ocean.

This will be the fourth time we've moved. Sometimes I get tired of moving. When we came here, I missed my old friends. I was sure I would never make new ones. Guess what happened! I made better friends than before.

I really like this town. Sometimes I wish we would just stay in one place. Then I remember how much I like traveling. I can't wait to jump into the wagon. I'm like Pa, I guess. I always want to know what's around the corner.

This time we're moving to the Dakota Territory. I wonder if I'll find new friends again. When we get there, I'll let you know.

Love,
Jimmy

from "Pioneer Schools"

Children in pioneer schools learned only a few subjects. Reading, writing, and math were most important. Students also learned history. Much of the school day was spent memorizing. Students learned math facts and poems by heart. They learned dates and grammar rules by heart, too.

Cities Then and Now

Vocabulary Words

afloat **re**use **un**known goods opportunities settlements

[1] Long ago, people roamed the land. They hunted animals or gathered berries for food. They did not live in cities. Over time, people learned to grow their own crops and raise animals. Families settled on land and built homes. More and more people began to live closer together in small settlements.

[2] Settlements included places where people could trade. Farmers would bring goods that they had raised to trade for goods that other people had made. Trading was one way people could get things they needed to live.

[3] Settlements grew and became cities. People from far away would travel to the city to trade. Roads and rivers made it easier for people to travel to the city. Roads, rivers, and oceans also made it easier to move goods from one place to another. Goods carried into cities on wagons or afloat on ships became a common sight.

[4] When settlers first came to America, they lived on the land. They farmed and hunted. Slowly, they began to build cities. They, too, built their cities near rivers, roads, and oceans. Later, the railroad helped cities to grow.

[5] Cities are important centers of trade. People go to the city to buy and sell goods. Cities also have many job opportunities. People need jobs in order to buy the things they need to live. Today millions of people live, work, and play in cities. Cities are still located where there are rivers, oceans, highways, and railroads. Now there are also airports in cities. All these ways to move goods make it easier to trade.

GO ON

Cities Then and Now (continued)

[6] Cities are now bigger than ever. People still make many things. They have also learned to reuse things to help take care of the earth. The future of cities is unknown. But they will probably become bigger and better.

Trading Goods in Memphis

Most cities grow because they are good places to trade goods. Memphis is one of those cities. Memphis is in the state of Tennessee on the mighty Mississippi River. Memphis is in the center of the United States. That makes it a good place to send and receive goods from all across the country. Railroad tracks and highways run through the area. Memphis also has a big airport. Memphis has become a major city for trade. Goods come into and out of the city every day.

from "Cities Then and Now"

When settlers first came to America, they lived on the land. They farmed and hunted. Slowly, they began to build cities. They, too, built their cities near rivers, roads, and oceans. Later, the railroad helped cities to grow.

Waking Up in the City

Vocabulary Words

busi**est** walk**er** quick**ly** graffiti mail carrier subway

1 Jorge woke to the sound of the garbage truck. He jumped out of bed. It was time to start a new day.

2 Jorge blinked as he peered out the window at his neighborhood. The neighbors always seemed busiest in the morning. He could see Mr. Alvarez making donuts through the window of his bake shop. Mrs. Diaz was sweeping her front steps.

3 It was almost time to pick up Mrs. Delgado's dog. Jorge earned extra money as a dog walker. It was fun and he liked helping his older neighbors.

4 Quickly, Jorge showered and got dressed. He went into the kitchen to help his mom make breakfast.

5 "Oh, no!" said Mom. "We are out of milk. Can you go to the corner market for me?"

6 "Sure," said Jorge. "I'll go to the market. I'll be right back."

7 As Jorge made his way to the store, he noticed some fresh graffiti on the sidewalk. He also saw businessmen and women walking to the subway on their way to work.

8 "Hello, Mr. Stern," he called out to the flower shop owner. Mr. Stern was setting out fresh flowers for sale.

9 Next, he saw a local artist setting up shop on the sidewalk. Street scenes of the city were lined up on a small table in front of her.

10 Finally, Jorge made it to the store. "Have a good day, Mrs. Chin," Jorge said as he paid for the milk.

Waking Up in the City (continued)

[11] On the way home, Jorge waved at the mail carrier, who had begun his rounds. As he walked along, Jorge looked in the store windows. He spotted the boots he wanted to buy when he saved enough money. Then Jorge bounded up the steps of his apartment building.

[12] "I love living in the city, Mom," Jorge said as he walked back into the kitchen. "Everything that you could ever want is right outside your door."

from "Waking Up in the City"

Quickly, Jorge showered and got dressed. He went into the kitchen to help his mom make breakfast.

"Oh, no!" said Mom. "We are out of milk. Can you go to the corner market for me?"

"Sure," said Jorge. "I'll go to the market. I'll be right back."

Reread the entire story "Waking Up in the City." Think about what you have read. What do you think Jorge will do next? Write two predictions. Give reasons for each prediction.

	Prediction	Why I think so
1		
2		

Making Predictions

Read each book title. Write a prediction telling what you think the book is about.

1. Bees and Beekeepers ______________________________

2. Journey Across the Ocean ______________________________

3. Mom and Me on Vacation ______________________________

4. My Favorite Baseball Team ______________________________

5. Into the Woods ______________________________

Visiting a New City

Vocabulary Words

guidebook advice attend amusement display sightseeing

[1] Let's pretend that you are going to a new city today. How do you find out about all the fun things to do? How will you get around the city if you do not have a car? What would be a good plan for your day?

[2] There are several ways to find out about a city. One way is to buy a guidebook or borrow one from a library. A guidebook tells you where to stay and eat, and what to see and do. You could also search for ideas on the Internet. Another way would be to look at the newspaper or to ask the advice of someone who is familiar with the city.

[3] How do you get around in a city without a car? Cities have taxis and buses. Some have subways, streetcars, and trolleys. You could also walk.

[4] Start your day by wandering around the city. Window-shop, look at interesting buildings, or go to a zoo or park. The park is a great place to skate, picnic, or fly a kite. Some cities have amusement parks. An amusement park has rides, food, games, shows, and shops. What fun!

[5] Don't forget to take some time to stop for lunch. A city always has lots of good places to eat. Try a new dish or a different type of food.

[6] You could spend your afternoon at a museum. Art and history museums have paintings, statues, and old objects on display. Some cities have special museums like the Chicago Children's Museum or the Rock and Roll Hall of Fame and Museum in Cleveland.

Visiting a New City (continued)

[7] After a long day of sightseeing, you could attend a play or a concert, or see a movie. Then enjoy the lights of the city from your room. Finally, go to bed and dream of what you might do in the city tomorrow.

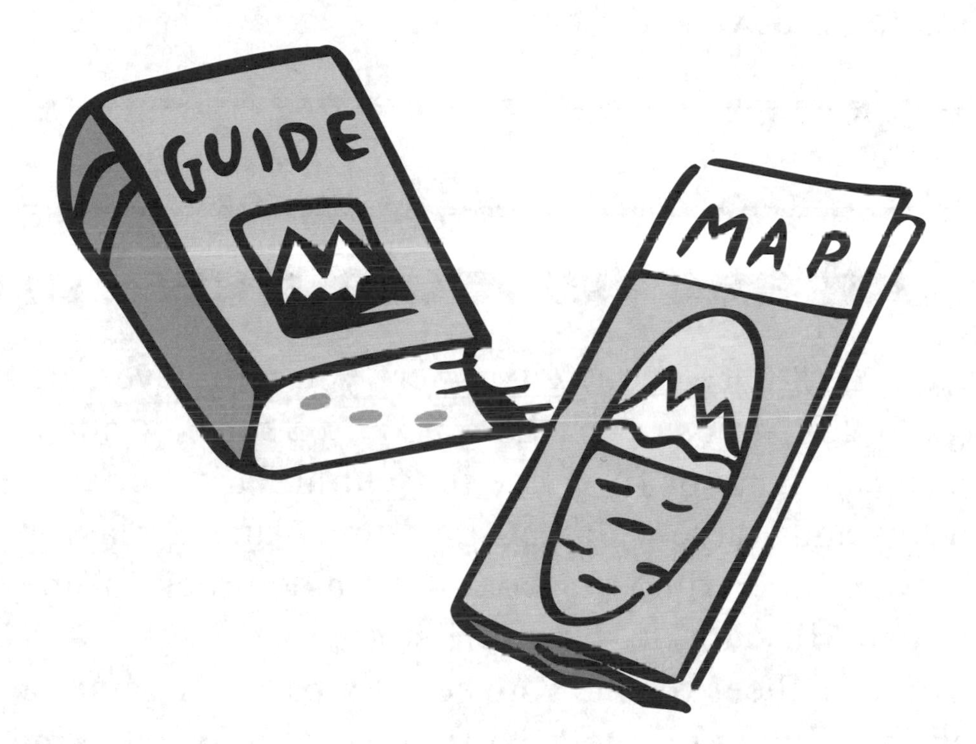

from "Visiting a New City"

There are several ways to find out about a city. One way is to buy a guidebook or borrow one from a library. A guidebook tells you where to stay and eat, and what to see and do. You could also search for ideas on the Internet. Another way would be to look at the newspaper or to ask the advice of someone who is familiar with the city.

Out and About in New York

New York City is one city where you will never run out of things to do. Almost everything is only a subway ride away!

You can skate or fly a kite in Central Park. See the paintings and statues at an art museum. Catch a play on Broadway. Study dinosaur bones and moon rocks at the American Museum of Natural History.

You can cheer for the Yankees at a baseball game or watch the filming of a television show. Sample any kind of food that your heart desires. Visit New York and have a great time!

The Family Store

Vocabulary Words

middle dinner tomorrow album concentrate hardware

[1] Suki sat next to her grandfather on the couch to look at the old picture album. He loved telling Suki about how they started their family store, Tanaka's General Store.

[2] "This is how the store looked on the day it opened in 1947," said Grandfather. "It was a general store. We sold everything from groceries and tools to clothing and shoes."

[3] "I like seeing how you looked when you were young, Grandfather," said Suki. "I also like looking at the funny old cars in the picture."

[4] "When I got older, we added the gas station and service garage. I just loved working on cars," said Grandfather. He showed her the picture of the day they opened the gas station.

[5] "Over time, department stores and supermarkets opened downtown so we stopped carrying groceries and clothing," Grandfather went on.

[6] He turned the page. Suki noticed a picture where the store name had changed. It had become a hardware store only and not a general store. The gas station and garage were also still there.

[7] "Today," said Suki as she turned the page, "we have a car parts store, a gas station, and a garage. Why did we get out of the hardware business, Grandfather?"

[8] "You know that your father and I both love cars," said Grandfather. "So we decided to concentrate on that part of the business and let the rest go. Being in the middle of downtown has helped us stay in business all these years."

GO ON

The Family Store (continued)

[9] Grandfather looked from the picture album to Suki. "I hope one of my grandchildren will want to take over the business one day."

[10] "Don't worry, Grandfather," said Suki. "I love cars, too. I think I would like to run things one day."

[11] "I know that I will be proud when you do. Well, it's almost time for dinner," said Grandfather. "Let's go set the table. We can look at more pictures tomorrow."

from "The Family Store"

"You know that your father and I both love cars," said Grandfather. "So we decided to concentrate on that part of the business and let the rest go. Being in the middle of downtown has helped us stay in business all these years."

Hot and Cool Miami

Have you ever been to Miami, Florida? It is a great place to enjoy the sand and sun. It is also a cool place to see the rich and famous. Many famous people call Miami home.

Long ago, Miami began as a small settlement of Native Americans on the Miami River. But one day, the Spanish arrived. Over time, settlers from Spain and other countries made their way to the area.

Miami became a center for trade between South America and North America. Railroad lines were built, and it grew to become a popular vacation spot. Miami also became the gateway to the United States for Cuban immigrants.

Today, people still go to Miami to enjoy the sun and sand. They drive down streets lined with palm trees and enjoy its famous pink and green buildings. People come from all over the world!

Where We Live—Biomes and Habitats

Vocabulary Words

climate   habitat   examine   organism   shelter   underground

[1] Climate is what the weather is like in a certain place over a very long time. How would you describe the climate where you live? Is it cold, hot, wet, dry, or mild? Earth's climate changes from place to place. Different plants and animals live in different climates. As a result, there are many biomes.

[2] Biomes are places on Earth that have the same kinds of climates, plants, and animals. Let's examine some different biomes. Biomes can be deserts, forests, or bodies of water. They can be other places, too, like cold places or swamps.

[3] Biomes are very different. Tundra biomes have very cold and dry climates. Deserts are dry, too. But they are most often hot, not cold. Rain forests are hot and wet. Some biomes are in oceans, rivers, and lakes. Plants and animals in each biome live together and depend on one another.

[4] An organism is any living thing. People, plants, and animals are all organisms. Organisms find ways to live in their biome's climate. For example, kangaroo rats live in the hot and dry desert biome. They make their homes underground. They stay in their homes during the very hot daytime. They come out at night when it is cooler. Then they hunt for food and water.

[5] Plants and animals also live in the icy tundra. Plants are small and grow close to the ground. This helps keep them safe from the very cold climate. Animals in these places usually have thick fur to keep them warm.

Where We Live (continued)

[6] An organism's home is called its habitat. A habitat provides all the things that the plant, animal, or person needs to live. This includes water, food, and shelter. What can you tell about your habitat?

[7] Some animals change habitats during their lives. For example, some frogs are born in water. When they grow up, they live mostly on land. People may change habitats many times during their lives.

from "Where We Live"

Biomes are places on Earth that have the same kinds of climates, plants, and animals. Let's examine some different biomes. Biomes can be deserts, forests, or bodies of water. They can be other places, too, like cold places or swamps.

Main idea: ____________________

____

Little Ant's Day

[1] It was time for Little Ant to start the day. He stretched and yawned. He had a long day of labor ahead of him. He looked around the ant nest. All the other worker ants were waking up, too.

Main idea: ____________________

____

[2] The worker ants went to work. They lined up and paraded down the tree trunk. "Find food!" shouted the lead ant. All the ants moved quickly to the edge of the grassy field.

Main idea: ____________________

____

[3] "I think that I can gather more grass seeds than you can," Little Ant said to his friends, as he did every day. Back and forth they went, working throughout the day. The little ant and his friends moved grass seeds to the nest. And so it went every day. Every day, the workers did their part for the colony.

Main idea: ____________________

____

Jane Goodall—a Biography

Vocabulary Words

institute **pre**judge **pre**caution humans improve scientist

[1] In 1960, Jane Goodall arrived in East Africa. Visitors did not come to this place very often. It had many wild animals. But it was Jane's dream. Jane had loved animals ever since she was a child. She dreamed about living with animals in the woods and writing about them.

[2] One day, Jane met Dr. Louis Leakey. He was a scientist who had worked in East Africa. Dr. Leakey asked Jane to go to a rain forest in Africa. He wanted her to watch chimpanzees in their habitat. He made a statement that would correctly prejudge Jane's work. He said that Jane would make a difference in the world.

[3] The chimpanzees lived in a forest in Tanzania, Africa. At first, the chimps were afraid of Jane. They ran away. This precaution was their way to stay safe from people.

[4] Soon the chimps became unafraid of Jane. They let her watch them. She gave them names, and they became friends. Jane watched the chimps hunt and share their food. She discovered that they made and used tools. Before this, people had thought that only humans made and used tools. She found out that the chimps were very smart.

[5] Jane's study is about the way animals act. Her study tells others about the chimps. It is the longest study of its kind in the world.

GO ON

Jane Goodall (continued)

[6] The Jane Goodall Institute was started in Jane's name. The people at the institute want to improve life on Earth. They believe that everyone can make a difference for all living things. They want to make things better for people and animals.

[7] People around the world know of Jane's work. She has won many awards for her good works. She has written many books, too. Today, she travels around the world. She speaks to school children and other people about making a difference in our world.

from "Jane Goodall"

In 1960, Jane Goodall arrived in East Africa. Visitors did not come to this place very often. It had many wild animals. But it was Jane's dream. Jane had loved animals ever since she was a child. She dreamed about living with animals in the woods and writing about them.

Main idea: ______________________________

____

Tropical Rain Forests

[1] Rain forests have very wet and warm climates. It is almost always raining in a rain forest. There are many trees and plants. The plants produce much of the oxygen in the air that we breathe.

Main idea: ______________________________

____

[2] Millions of animals and plants live in rain forests. Many live in the canopy of the forest. The canopy is the top leafy parts of the trees. This place is full of insects, birds, and mammals. The forest floor is the bottom part of the forest. Many large and small animals live on the floor, too.

Main idea: ______________________________

____

Frog in the Well—a Chinese Fable

Vocabulary Words

preview **dis**please **dis**appear bragged marvelous realized

[1] A long time ago, Frog lived in a shallow well. His well was not very deep. One day, Turtle crawled by Frog's well. "Turtle, come into my home," invited Frog.

[2] "My well is so marvelous!" Frog croaked. "Let me give you a preview of what you will find here. The water is so shallow that it only comes up to your neck. You can float all around on your back. You can push your feet against the bottom and leap around in the water."

[3] Frog strutted around in front of Turtle like a king. "I am the king of this well," he bragged.

[4] Turtle looked at Frog for a few seconds. Then he said, "My friend, I can see your happiness. I can tell that you think your home is the best place ever."

[5] Frog stuck out his chest proudly and beamed at Turtle. Turtle started to climb into the well. Then he became stuck. With help from Frog, Turtle pulled his body back out of the opening.

[6] "I hate to displease you, Frog," said Turtle. "But your well is not the greatest place to live."

[7] Then Turtle began to tell about his wonderful home in the ocean. "The sea is so wide that you can't see to the end of it. It is so deep that no turtle has ever seen the bottom," he said. "The waters never disappear, even if it doesn't rain for a long time," Turtle explained. "The ocean doesn't flood the land when it rains a lot. The ocean is the greatest habitat!"

Frog in the Well (continued)

[8] Frog was speechless. He suddenly understood just how small his well was. He realized how much more there was in the world.

[9] Frog learned a very important lesson that day. He learned not to brag about having the best of anything.

from "Frog in the Well"

Then Turtle began to tell about his wonderful home in the ocean. "The sea is so wide that you can't see to the end of it. It is so deep that no turtle has ever seen the bottom," he said. "The waters never disappear, even if it doesn't rain for a long time," Turtle explained. "The ocean doesn't flood the land when it rains a lot. The ocean is the greatest habitat!"

Main idea: ______________________________

____

Oceans

[1] Oceans cover most of the earth. There are five main oceans. They are the Pacific, the Atlantic, the Arctic, the Indian, and the Southern Oceans. They are all connected to each other. You can sail in a boat from ocean to ocean.

Main idea: ______________________________

____

[2] The ocean is home to many animals. The smallest animals and the largest animals on the earth live there.

Main idea: ______________________________

____

[3] Oceans have salty water and waves. The waves are caused when wind blows the water. Stronger winds make bigger waves.

Main idea: ______________________________

____

How Animals Survive in the Desert

Vocabulary Words

discomfort **ex**cess **ex**treme barren hibernate survive

[1] Many animals live in the desert. Deserts are usually dry and barren. They get little, if any, rainfall each year. Only hardy plants grow there. How do you think animals live in places that are so dry?

[2] Many deserts are very hot, too. Animals in the desert face much discomfort. They must find ways to live with extreme heat. They have scarce water and food, too.

[3] There are three main ways that animals survive in the desert. They hide from the heat, find water, and store water.

Hide from the Heat

[4] One way desert animals survive is to stay away from heat. Some animals search for food during times when it is not so hot. Birds fly out at dawn and just before the sun sets in the evening. Other animals sleep during the day when there is an excess of heat. Some of these animals are foxes, bats, snakes, and rats. They go out at night to look for food and water.

[5] Some desert animals go deep under the ground to stay cool. They hibernate until the rains come. They sleep for long periods of time.

[6] Some lizards move quickly over the hot sand to stay away from the heat. They stop under rocks or cactus leaves. They cool their bodies in the shade of the plants.

GO ON

How Animals Survive in the Desert (continued)

Find Water

[7] Another way animals live in the desert is by finding water. Cactus plants and other plants hold a lot of water in their leaves and stems. Some animals get all their water from the cactus, other plants, and seeds. Some animals, such as the kangaroo rats, never drink water. Their bodies make water from dry seeds.

Store Water

[8] Some desert animals store water in their bodies. The gila monster is a type of lizard. It stores fat and water in its tail. It stores fat and water so that it can survive the long dry periods.

from "How Animals Survive in the Desert"

One way desert animals survive is to stay away from heat. Some animals search for food during times when it is not so hot. Birds fly out at dawn and just before the sun sets in the evening. Other animals sleep during the day when there is an excess of heat. Some of these animals are foxes, bats, snakes, and rats. They go out at night to look for food and water.

Main idea: ____

____

Deserts

[1] Deserts have very little rain. There are many months when it doesn't rain at all in the desert. And when it does rain, it pours. Even the wettest deserts get less than 10 inches of rain a year, though.

Main idea: ____

____

[2] Deserts are places of extreme temperatures. Most deserts have very hot days and cool nights. But some deserts are very cold places. They are dry like the hot deserts. But they have cold weather and ice.

Main idea: ____

____

Reptiles—What Are They?

Vocabulary Words

exterior **mis**judge **mis**understood environment hinge poisonous

[1] Some people misjudge reptiles. Reptiles are not cute and furry. They don't look like other animals. They look prehistoric. That's no surprise. Reptiles have been around for a long time. Scientists think they have been on Earth for more than 3 million years. But there's no need to fear most reptiles.

[2] There are many different kinds of reptiles. They come in all shapes and sizes. Turtles are reptiles. So are snakes and lizards. Crocodiles and alligators are reptiles. Some scientists call birds and dinosaurs reptiles, too. Reptiles look mysterious. In ancient times, some people treated them like gods. Don't be misled by their looks. There's nothing mysterious about reptiles. Like all animals, they're just trying to survive.

[3] Different kinds of reptiles have some things in common. All reptiles have spines, or backbones. Most reptiles lay eggs. Their skin is covered with scales. Scales protect the reptile, but they don't hold in much heat. Reptiles need to keep warm. They do this by going to a warm place. That's why we call them cold-blooded. And that's why you see reptiles lying in the sun. Reptiles never need dentists, either. When their teeth fall out, new ones grow in.

[4] Some reptiles have special talents. Snakes can stretch their mouths very wide. They can swallow a whole meal in one gulp. Turtles have a good trick, too. They can pull their heads and legs into their shell. Their soft bodies stay safe inside. Their hard exterior makes it tough for other animals to eat them. The eastern box turtle can do even more. That turtle's shell has a hinge. It can close its shell like a door.

Reptiles—What Are They? (continued)

[5] Reptiles are often misunderstood. Only a few are dangerous, though. You know you should stay away from the big, snapping jaws of an alligator. Some people live around poisonous snakes. If you are one of those people, you should learn what they look like. But most reptiles are harmless. They help the environment. Get to know reptiles. You'll see that they're fascinating. There is no need to be afraid of most reptiles.

Interesting Iguanas

Iguanas are interesting creatures. They don't seem to do much, but they know how to fill up their days. Iguanas like to climb trees and bask in the sun with other iguanas. They rest in the trees and look around. When iguanas are not resting, they are hunting for food. They like to eat flowers and leaves. Iguanas must like variety. They eat more than forty kinds of plants. They may even eat a bug or two once in a while. Iguanas also like swimming. They dive under the water. Sometimes they stay underwater for thirty minutes at one time. Then they sit in the sun and get warm.

New title: ______________________________

Main idea: ______________________________

____

from "Reptiles— What Are They?"

Different kinds of reptiles have some things in common. All reptiles have spines, or backbones. Most reptiles lay eggs. Their skin is covered with scales. Scales protect the reptile, but they don't hold in much heat. Reptiles need to keep warm. They do this by going to a warm place. That's why we call them cold-blooded. And that's why you see reptiles lying in the sun. Reptiles never need dentists, either. When their teeth fall out, new ones grow in.

Main idea: ______________________________

____

Why Rattlesnakes Bite

Vocabulary Words

mistreated kind**ness** fierce**ness** attention rhythm slithered

[1] Long ago, Rattle the rattlesnake was friendly. Rattle liked people, and people liked him. People liked his kindness. They thought he was always cheerful. Most of all, they liked his rattle. When Rattle slithered into town, people felt happy. Grown-ups worked faster to the rattle's cheerful beat. Teenagers liked the rhythm, too. They could dance to it. Babies liked Rattle most of all. Whenever they saw Rattle, they giggled.

[2] At first, Rattle liked the attention. Then things started to change. People wanted to hear the rattle all the time. If Rattle sat quietly, they poked him. When Rattle tried to take a nap, they shook him. Soon Rattle got very tired. He wasn't cheerful and friendly any more. He felt very grumpy. But Rattle never wanted to bite anyone.

[3] Rattle moved more slowly. His rattle moved slowly, too. Grown-ups were used to working to the rattle's rhythm. Their work slowed down. Teenagers missed the happy beat, too. No more fast dancing! Now they could only waltz. The babies forgot about Rattle. Only one baby knew something was missing. She just wasn't sure what it was. She kept looking at Rattle curiously.

[4] One day Rattle got so tired, he felt asleep right in town. No one noticed him except that one small baby. The baby picked up the sleeping snake and shook him. Rattle woke up. He was in the air. He was too tired to know what he was doing. He bit the baby. Luckily, Rattle's poison wasn't strong.

GO ON

Why Rattlesnakes Bite (continued)

[5] After that, no one liked Rattle. People ignored him. Some even mistreated him. Rattle felt lonely. He grew mean and bitter. The more bitter he got, the stronger his poison got. Rattle's children turned out just like him. Today rattlesnakes don't like people, and people don't like the rattlesnake's fierceness. People run when they hear a rattle, and rattlesnakes are glad! And now you know why rattlesnakes bite.

from "Reptiles— What Are They?"

Reptiles are often misunderstood. Only a few are dangerous, though. You know you should stay away from the big, snapping jaws of an alligator. Some people live around poisonous snakes. If you are one of those people, you should learn what they look like. But most reptiles are harmless. They help the environment. Get to know reptiles. You'll see that they're fascinating. There is no need to be afraid of most reptiles.

Write the answers to these questions.

1. Who or what is the paragraph about? ______________________

____

2. What is the most important thing about the who or the what?

____

____

____

3. What is the main idea of the paragraph? ______________________

____

____

Rattlesnakes

Your chances of being bitten by a rattlesnake are very slim. In fact, you may never even see one. That's because rattlers stay near their dens. They hunt mostly at night. They stay away from people. Rattlers only bite if they feel trapped. Before biting, they shake their rattles. The rattle is a warning. It means "go away!" If you pay attention, the rattler won't bite.

Write the answers to these questions.

1. Who or what is the paragraph about? ______________________

____

2. What is the most important thing about the who or the what?

____

____

____

3. What is the main idea of the paragraph? ______________________

____

____

Reptiles as Pets

Vocabulary Words

happi**ness** care**less** heart**less** reputable responsibly sleek

[1] Many people find happiness living with pets. The most common pets are cats and dogs. Some people enjoy fish, birds, or hamsters. Reptiles are popular pets with some people, too.

[2] Would you expect reptiles to be easy pets? Do you think that most reptiles stay in one place and don't mess up the house? Some people do think just that. They are sure that reptiles don't need much care. People who think reptiles are easy to care for are in for a shock.

[3] Are you thinking about getting a pet reptile? If so, you need to know a few facts first. Some reptiles live a long time. Turtles can live thirty years or longer. An iguana that is well cared for can live over twenty years. Many snakes live from fifteen to twenty years, too. Also, keep in mind that some reptiles can grow quite large. A cute little iguana may someday be six feet long.

[4] Do you still want a pet reptile? Then take some time to learn. Read all about the pet you want. Find out how long it lives and how big it will get. Find out what it eats and what kind of home it needs. Find out how much time you'll need to spend.

[5] If you still want a reptile after learning all about it, go to a reputable pet store. Make sure the store is clean. Then choose the healthiest reptile. Sometimes it's hard to tell when a reptile is sick. Learn what to look for. A reptile's eyes should be clear. Its scales should be sleek and flat. It should move easily.

GO ON

Reptiles as Pets (continued)

[6] Once you get your new pet, don't get careless with it. Your new pet is depending on you. Not to care for it responsibly would be heartless. Remember to feed your pet and clean out its home often. If your pet needs sun, put its home in a sunny place. Keeping your pet healthy and happy will make you happy, too.

Two Kinds of Snakes

[1] Boa constrictors and garter snakes are two kinds of snakes. Many reptiles lay eggs, but the boa constrictor and the garter snake do not. Both snakes bear their young alive. Boa constrictors may give birth to 50 snakes at one time. The garter snake usually gives birth to about 18 snakes at one time.

[2] Neither snake is poisonous. Both the boa constrictor and the garter snake defend themselves by striking. That means that they throw their heads at their enemies.

[3] How do the two kinds of snakes compare in size? A newborn boa is only about 15 inches long, but it can grow up to 14 feet! In contrast, a full-grown garter snake usually is no more than 30 inches long.

More About Garter Snakes

There are 13 different kinds of garter snakes, and none of them is dangerous to people. Most garter snakes have three stripes that run down their bodies. Some have a pattern that fills in the area between the stripes. Some don't. Females are usually longer than males.

Alike	Different

Alligator or Crocodile?

Vocabulary Words

fear**less** dread**ful** power**ful** creature fang glands

[1] Imagine you're in South Florida. The area is swampy. Tall grass is all around you. Suddenly you hear a sound. You stare at the grass. The grass parts. A face is staring back at you. The face is dreadful. This is the biggest reptile you've ever seen. And it has a long, powerful tail. This is no time to stop and ask whether you're looking at an alligator or a crocodile. Just in case you're feeling fearless, though, here are some ways to tell.

[2] Are you near salt water? Then you might be looking at a crocodile. Crocs don't mind salt water. They have glands that help them survive in salt water. Alligators sometimes swim in salt water, too. Gators can't stay very long, though. They don't have the same glands.

[3] Check the animal's color. Is it grayish black? If so, the animal is probably an older gator. Is the animal's hide black? Does it have little touches of yellow or white? That's a gator, too, but it's younger. Is it tan or brown? The animal is probably a croc.

[4] The real clue is in the beast's face. A gator's snout is blunt and rounded. A croc's snout is longer and sharper. Both gators and crocs have lots of sharp teeth. At this point, you'd better hope the creature has its mouth closed. If it does, look for teeth. When a gator's mouth is closed, you can't see the teeth. A croc's teeth do show when its mouth is closed. Look for a long fang. The fang sticks up from the side of the croc's lower jaw.

Alligator or Crocodile? (continued)

[5] Both crocs and gators are very shy. Unless they've been fed by people or are guarding their nest, they're likely to run away. Crocs are even shyer than gators. Hardly anyone ever sees a crocodile. So if you're looking into the face of a big reptile, it's probably an alligator.

The Great Turtle Race

[1] Chuck looked for his pet turtle. Skimmer was in the corner of the aquarium with his head tucked into his shell. "We need to find something interesting for you to do," Chuck said.

[2] Chuck had an idea. He and his friend Stevie would race their pet turtles. Chuck drew a chalk circle on the driveway. The boys carefully set their turtles down in the middle.

[3] It was hard to tell the turtles apart. They were exactly the same size, but each boy knew his own pet. Sleepy had a small yellow spot on his shell. Skimmer did not. Sleepy's tail was shorter than Skimmer's tail, too.

[4] "Go, Sleepy!" yelled Stevie.

[5] "Cross that line, Skimmer!" yelled Chuck. Skimmer looked around. Then he started to plod back and forth. He almost crossed the line, but he turned and went back. Meanwhile, Sleepy lived up to his name. Finally, Skimmer walked in the right direction.

[6] "The winner!" Chuck called out. Was it Chuck's imagination? Or did Skimmer look proud of his win?

Complete the Venn diagram.

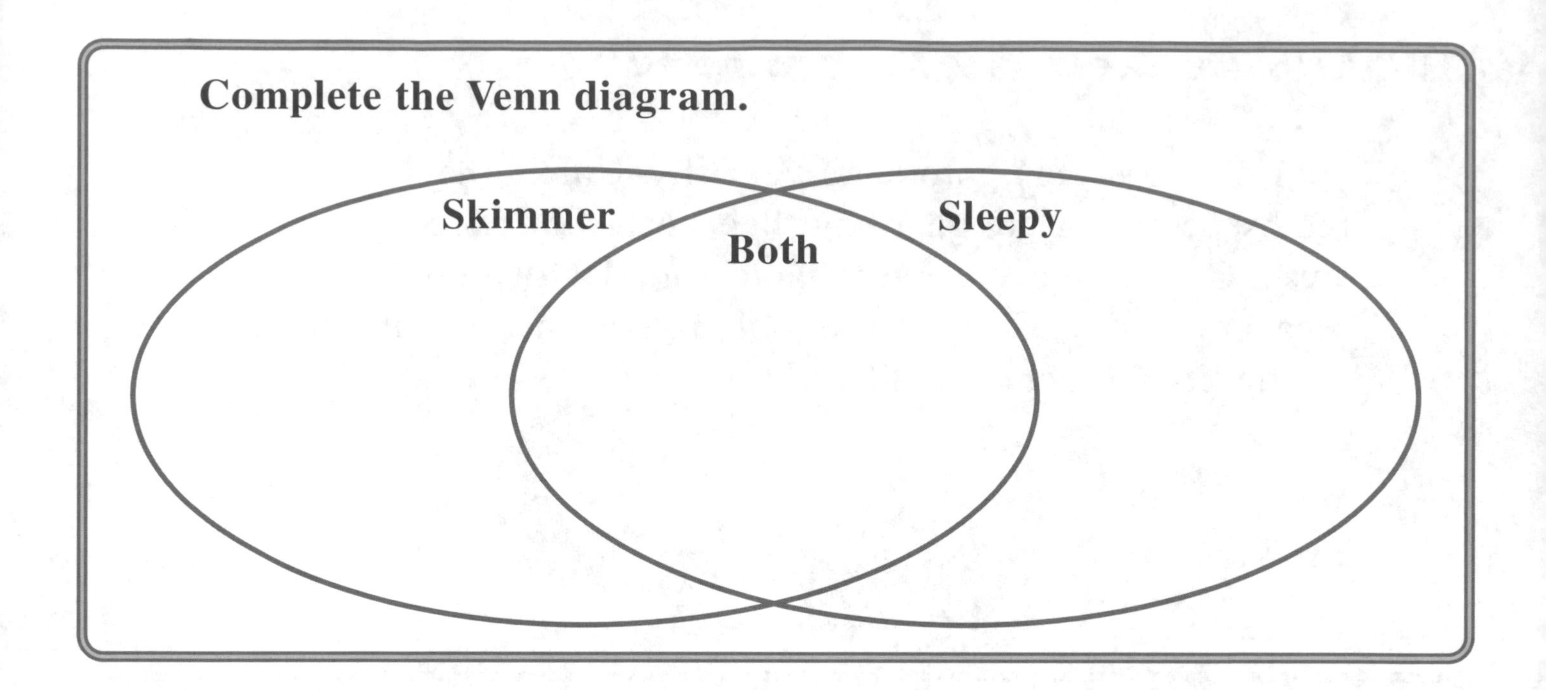

from "Alligator or Crocodile?"

The real clue is in the beast's face. A gator's snout is blunt and rounded. A croc's snout is longer and sharper. Both gators and crocs have lots of sharp teeth. At this point, you'd better hope the creature's mouth is still closed. If it is, look for teeth. When a gator's mouth is closed, you can't see them. A croc's teeth do show when its mouth is closed. Look for a long fang. The fang sticks up from the side of the croc's lower jaw.

Complete the Venn diagram.

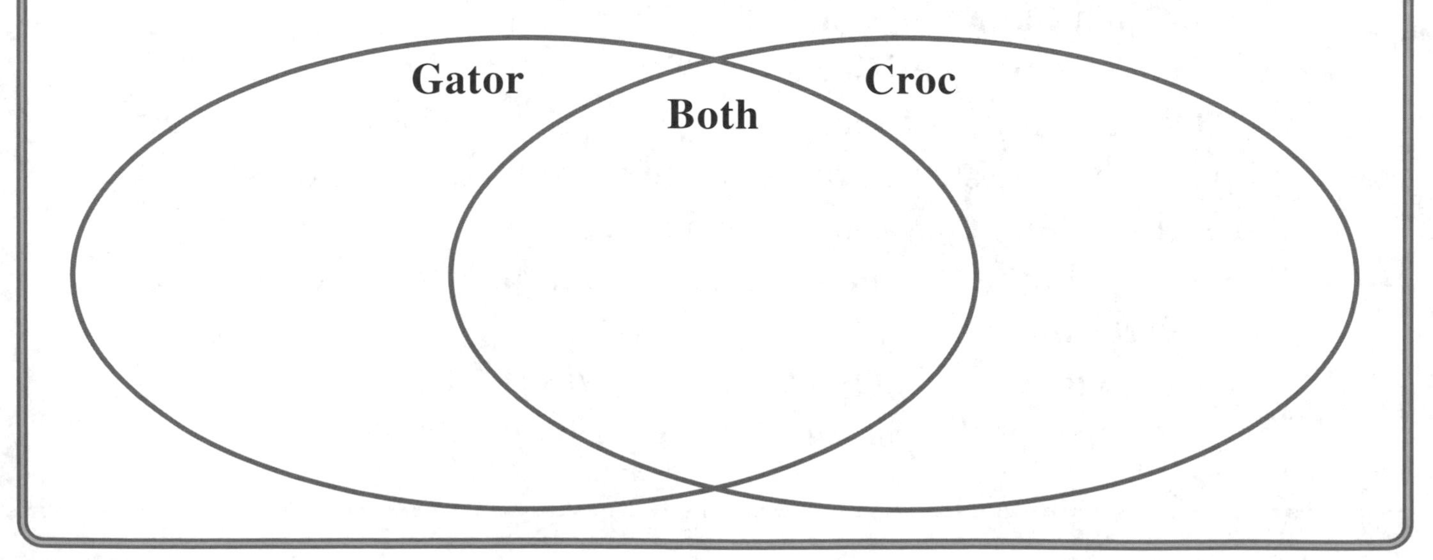

Mammals Large and Small

Vocabulary Words

use**ful** complete**ly** **un**likely fuel nourish region

[1] There are about 4,000 kinds of mammals in the world. People, dogs, cats, whales, kangaroos, anteaters, and bats are all examples of mammals. The largest mammal to ever live on Earth is the blue whale. This powerful mammal is over 100 feet long. The smallest mammal is the hog-nosed bat from Thailand. It is about the size of a bumblebee.

[2] Some mammals have lots of hair, and some have only a little hair. Some mammals have long hair that completely covers their bodies, like cats and goats. Some mammals have very short hair—so short that it just looks like fuzz. Even whales that swim underwater have some hair. You would have to look closely at a baby whale's lips to see the hair, but it is there!

[3] It doesn't matter whether the weather is hot or cold, a mammal has the ability to keep its body at a constant temperature. It does this by burning food as fuel. As unbelievable as it may sound, a region of the brain works to control the temperature. The warm blood helps mammals live in many different climates. Some mammals, such as polar bears, live in very cold places. Other mammals, such as camels, live in very hot places.

[4] Most mammal babies live inside their mothers before they are born. Cows, horses, elephants, cats, dogs—all these mammal mothers give birth to live babies. Only three kinds of mammals have babies that hatch from eggs. An anteater and a duck-billed platypus are examples of mammals that lays eggs.

GO ON

Mammals Large and Small (continued)

[5] One mammal mother carries her babies around in a pouch until they are quite large. It may seem unlikely, but it's true. The useful pouch is like a pocket that is part of the mother's body. Do you know a kind of mammal that does this? If you named a kangaroo or a koala, you are right!

[6] Mammal mothers nourish their babies with milk. Even bats, whales, and koala bears drink milk when they are babies. The mammal mother cares for her babies until they can find their own food and sometimes even longer. Human parents take care of their young for many years!

from "Mammals Large and Small"

Some mammals have lots of hair, and some have only a little hair. Some mammals have long hair that completely covers their bodies, like cats and goats. Some mammals have very short hair—so short that it just looks like fuzz. Even whales that swim underwater have some hair. You would have to look closely at a baby whale's lips to see the hair, but it is there!

More About Mammals

[1] Many animals that live in very cold areas have short, stocky limbs. This keeps them low to the ground where they can stay warmer. They have thick fur. Some of them have fur that changes color to match the season. This helps them hide from dangerous animals.

[2] Many animals that live in very hot, dry places are small. Smaller animals don't need as much food or water. Many of the animals don't have to drink water. They get the water they need from the plants they eat. Then they store it in their bodies. Most are light in color.

MAMMALS	
Cold Areas	Hot Areas

Maggie's Eyes

Vocabulary Words

unattend**ed** sparkl**ed** discourag**ed** nervously demanding obstacles

[1] Maggie waited impatiently by the tree. She stepped nervously from one foot to another. She clutched her mother's arm. She just knew she was the happiest girl ever! She could hear Mr. Adams talking gently to the dog as he walked toward her. "Can you see Scout, Mother?" she said anxiously. "What does he look like?"

[2] Her mother's eyes sparkled as she described the large dog. "He has warm and friendly eyes," she said. "He has golden, silky hair."

[3] Maggie knows that Scout has been in training for months. He goes to a guide dog school. He has been trained to help people like her. Maggie is blind. Scout is a guide dog for people who cannot see. Scout is one of thousands of guide dogs who help blind people.

[4] People who are blind can move around in several ways. They can hold on to someone's arm, use a cane, or use a guide dog like Scout. Many blind people choose to use a guide dog who can be both friend and helper.

[5] Maggie and Scout will now train together. They will work together to get from place to place. Scout will learn the places that Maggie usually goes. Maggie will learn how to tell him how far to go and when to turn. He will learn to follow her directions.

[6] A good guide dog has to learn when to turn left and right. It has to know when to walk forward and when to stop. It has to avoid obstacles. Obstacles may be things like low branches or narrow walkways. A good guide dog has to stop at curbs, stairs, and crosswalks.

Maggie's Eyes (continued)

[7] Scout will have a very demanding job. Scout will wear a harness that Maggie holds. Scout will lead her safely throughout the day. He will put in a full day of work helping Maggie move safely from school to the market to her home. Scout will never leave her unattended when they are out and about.

[8] But when he goes home at night, Scout's harness comes off, and he becomes Maggie's best friend. If Maggie becomes discouraged, Scout will cheer her up. Maggie is very thankful to have such a good friend and helper as Scout.

from "Maggie's Eyes"

A good guide dog has to learn when to turn left and right. It has to know when to walk forward and when to stop. It has to avoid obstacles. Obstacles may be things like low branches or narrow walkways. A good guide dog has to stop at curbs, stairs, and crosswalks.

Main idea: ____

____

The Mouse and the Squirrel

[1] One day, a thirsty mouse scurried down to the river to get a drink of water. The water was rushing by very fast. The mouse slipped and slid down the bank.

[2] "Help, help!" he cried out to his friends on the bank. "I am drowning!" But his friends could not hear him.

[3] A squirrel was sitting in a nearby tree. She heard the mouse's cries for help. She broke off a branch from the tree and tossed it in the water. The mouse crawled onto the branch and floated safely to the bank.

[4] Later that week, the squirrel was sitting in a tree by the river. A hunter saw the squirrel and set up a trap to catch her. When the mouse saw this, he bit the hunter sharply on the leg. The hunter cried out in pain and ran away. The squirrel was safe.

Main idea: ____

____

Amazing Water Mammals

Vocabulary Words

rescu**ed** **un**friendl**y** **un**doubt**edly** echoes nimbly whistles

[1] Not all mammals live on land. Many mammals spend their entire life in water. But they are not fish. They do not have scales or gills. They are water mammals. Some types of water mammals are sea lions, whales, dolphins, seals, manatees, and sea otters.

[2] Like other mammals, water mammals breathe air. They must come to the top of water to get air, or they will die. Their babies live inside the mothers like all other mammals. When they are born, they drink milk from their mother's body. They are warm-blooded, too.

[3] Let's learn more about two water mammals. Undoubtedly, whales and dolphins are special creatures. Whales are very large animals that live in the ocean. The blue whale is the largest animal in the world. Whales travel in groups called "pods" to find food.

[4] Dolphins live with the whales in the ocean. Dolphins are much smaller than whales. No one would ever call dolphins unfriendly. The animals swim close to ships and seem to welcome guests. Dolphins are very fast swimmers. Some dolphins have been known to help animals and babies who are in danger. They have rescued injured animals and babies who have fallen into the ocean.

[5] Whales and dolphins are great divers. Their bodies move rapidly through the water. They can come nimbly to the surface of the water to breathe. They have flippers in the front of their bodies to guide them. They have powerful tails to move them. Under their skin, they have a layer of fat. This fat keeps them warm and helps them float.

GO ON

Amazing Water Mammals (continued)

[6] Some dolphins and whales make sounds, like clicks, squeaks, and whistles. These sounds are used to help them find their way in the water. They listen for echoes of their sounds. The echoes help them know where objects are located. Some scientists believe that these sounds are a kind of language. They think that the animals talk with each other.

from "Amazing Water Mammals"

Some dolphins and whales make sounds, like clicks, squeaks, and whistles. These sounds are used to help them find their way in the water. They listen for echoes of their sounds. The echoes help them know where objects are located. Some scientists believe that these sounds are a kind of language. They think that the animals talk with each other.

Main idea: ____

____

Endangered Mammals

Over 5,000 mammal and other animal groups are called *endangered.* What causes animal groups to disappear? Sometimes the climate of an area may change. The animals that live there can't adapt to the new temperatures. Sometimes food and water become scarce, and animals can't survive. Sometimes hunters or other stronger animals kill off the animals. Sometimes the animals' habitat is destroyed.

Main idea: ____

____

Mammals of Mystery

Vocabulary Words

scari**est** **mis**understood **un**appreciated consume radar typically

[1] What is the only mammal that can fly? No, it's not a flying squirrel. That mammal doesn't really fly. It only jumps and glides through the air. It's not a bird either. A bird can certainly fly, but a bird is not a mammal. The only mammal that can fly is a bat. Bats flap their wings and fly like a bird.

[2] The tiny mammals whoosh through the air in the dark of night searching for food. They are very swift and quiet. Some people think bats are mysterious and even a bit scary. Bats are very misunderstood and unappreciated!

[3] Bats live in many parts of the world. Like other mammals, bats are warm-blooded. They feed their babies milk. They have fur.

[4] But bats are different from other mammals in some ways. Bats are nocturnal. They sleep all day in a cave, barn, treetop, or other dark place. They typically like to sleep with a group of other bats, and the group is called a roost. Some roosts may have thousands of sleeping bats.

[5] Most bats make high noises called "bat radar." The sounds bounce off objects, and bats can tell where the object is. This helps bats fly at night. People and other mammals cannot hear these bat sounds.

Mammals of Mystery (continued)

[6] Nearly all bats that live in the United States eat insects, including pesky mosquitoes! They also feast on small reptiles and fruit. However, some bats in Central and South America drink blood. This is why some of the scariest stories are about vampire bats. But vampire bats do not attack people. They feed on the blood of resting animals, such as cows, pigs, and horses. And even then, vampire bats each only consume about 2 tablespoons of blood in a day.

from "Mammals of Mystery"

What is the only mammal that can fly? No, it's not a flying squirrel. That mammal jumps and glides through the air. It's not a bird either. A bird can certainly fly, but it is not a mammal. The only mammal that can fly is a bat. Bats flap their wings and fly like a bird.

Creatures of the Night

1 There are nearly 1,000 different kinds of bats. The hog-nosed bat is the world's smallest bat. It has a wing span of only about 2 inches. The flying fox bat is the world's largest bat. It has a wing span of up to 80 inches.

2 The saying "blind as a bat" is not true. Although their eyes are adapted to darkness, a bat is not blind. In fact, some can see as well as humans.

3 A bat's ears are very large compared to its head. This helps a bat pick up all the sounds as it flies at night.

4 Bats have arm and hand bones similar to most other mammals. But a bat has long fingers compared to its body. Its wings are stretched over the bat's arm and four fingers. The wings go all the way down the body. The skin on the wings looks delicate, but it is very strong. Bats can use their wings for other things than flying. They can hold insects, frogs, or fruit that they are eating.